I'm Not Retiring

Jake Adie

jadie

Published by
Jadie Books Limited 2006

Copyright © Jake Adie 2006

ISBN 0 9549354-4-6
ISBN 978 0 9549354-4-3

Cover illustration by Ian West

Typesetting by Jake Adie

Printed & bound by
York Publishing Services Ltd
64 Hallfield Road
Layerthorpe
York
YO31 7ZQ

This book is sold subject to the condition that it shall not, in any circumstances, be lent, resold, hired out or otherwise circulated without the publisher's prior consent in any form of binding or cover other than that in which it is published and without a similar condition including this condition being imposed on the subsequent purchaser.

For the slightly confused,
slightly obsolete,
slightly retired

Other Not Really Titles

I'm Not Really 30 (female edition)
I'm Not Really 30 (male edition)
I'm Not Really 40 (female edition)
I'm Not Really 40 (male edition)
I'm Not Really 50 (female edition)
I'm Not Really 50 (male edition)
I'm Not Really 60 (female edition)
I'm Not Really 60 (male edition)
I'm Not Really Pregnant
I'm Not Really Getting Married
I'm Not Really Moving House
It's Not Really Christmas

Me Retiring?

Now listen here, I don't intend to say this more than once. Ready? Right, I am not about to retire. Got that? Me. Retire. Not. Well, not yet anyway. Might get round to it one day. Bound to, I suppose. When I'm an old man most likely. Mm, when I'm ready to be a pensioner, God forbid. And not a day sooner. Understand? Too

I'm Not Really Retiring

bad if you don't because there's no way I'm hanging up my boots yet. After all, I've still got loads to do. Jobs to get finished. Deadlines to meet. Can't turn my back on them just like that. It's not the done thing. Wouldn't be right. People would feel I'd let them down. Not taken my responsibilities seriously. Not the reliable kind

Me Retiring?

of behaviour they'd come to expect from me. I mean, who else is going to do it? Mm, ever thought about that? No, of course you haven't. Hasn't occurred to you, has it? Well, think about it for a second. Think about the way things might be in this place if I weren't here. Yeah? See? Not so easy, eh? This place operating without my involvement? Don't make me laugh, please. It's a fierce market place out there. Lots of competition. Sharks ready to snap you in two. Vultures hovering overhead waiting to tear your guts out. Take it from me, companies don't survive by letting youngsters like me throw in the towel. I'm an

Me Retiring?

indispensable member of an important team. Take me away and the whole thing falls apart. No two ways about it. Essential cog in the wheel. Stop me operating and the machine will grind to a halt. The boss knows that. Must do. He'd have a pink fit if the thought entered his mind. There's no way he'd entertain the prospect for one minute. Anyway, people don't retire at my time of life. Do you think I haven't seen the types of folk who do that sort of thing? Course I have. I've even been to retirement dos. You know, presentations, that kind of thing. Gold watches, carriage clocks, microwave ovens. That's when you retire.

Me Retiring?

When you need things like that. Well I don't. Wouldn't mind a microwave perhaps. Mm, be handy, one of those. But not essential. No, got along all these years without one. Another few years won't hurt. However, I'm getting off the point. You see, if you start to dispense with key members of staff like me you'll only be left with the workplace full of juniors. We've got loads of them. Every company has. In fact, if I think about it I can remember most of them starting. Yes, their first days with the firm. God, some years ago now I must say but I can picture it as though it were only yesterday. Come to think of it, some of them must have been

I'm Not Really Retiring

Me Retiring?

with us for twenty or thirty years. Middle-aged juniors! Now there's something to get your head around. Amazing or what? But that's juniors for you. Same the world over I don't doubt. But where does that leave me, eh? If they're middle-aged, what am I? Never quite looked at it like that before. Must be sort of in between. Yes, that's it, an in-betweenie. Well it's better than one of those, what do you call them? . . .

I'm Not Really Retiring

OAPs?

They're positively ancient aren't they? Wonder they still manage to draw breath. God, imagine being one of them. And the funny thing is, they've all been around for absolutely ages. Yeah? Well certainly as long as I can remember. Used to see them as a kid. Never knew what they were, if I'm to be truthful. Wasn't until I got older that I actually realized they were the same species as us. Honest. Understandable if you ask me. All that wrinkly skin and miserable looking faces. And funny clothes. How should I have known that we were related? And their behaviour. Definitely a bit peculiar that.

OAPs?

Okay, I knew we shared the same kind of habitat. Weren't completely different I'll grant you. Had houses like ours. And appeared to eat similar food. Only similar. And, all right, they walked upright like us; bipeds. So, it took me a little time to fall in. Nothing wrong with that. I bet you weren't much different.

Anyway, what really confused me was the way they never seemed to go out very much. Preferred to stay indoors all week. Funny that. While the rest of us were out at school or work or the cinema or, well, anywhere really, they always seemed to be sitting at home. Well, you've got to admit it's rather odd. And then,

I'm Not Really Retiring

OAPs?

all of a sudden, for some totally inexplicable reason, the whole damn lot of them would don their hats and coats and make a beeline for the local post office. All at the same time. Completely clog the place up. Couldn't move for OAPs. And the poor old postmaster had no choice, did he? I mean, what would you do in his position.

You'd hand over the takings, right? That's why I thought they had nothing to do with us. The way they'd organise themselves. Working as a team. Looking after their own kind in a strange, totally selfless manner. Not one single member of their community ever appeared to want to get one over on their fellow OAPs. In an

I'm Not Really Retiring

OAPs?

incredibly orderly fashion, they'd see that the sum total of the cash in the postmaster's till was divided up fairly between the lot of them. No fuss. No threats. Just a simple share out. While the rest of us were out earning a crust. And no one ever seemed to want to do a thing about it. Didn't seem very fair to me. So, you can imagine how surprised I was when I later learned that the rest of us have to pay taxes to enable the post office's tills to be replenished to accommodate their weekly onslaught. Not a bad little number if you ask me. And that's exactly what I've been doing my whole working life. Toiling away from Monday morning until,

OAPs?

well, about Wednesday afternoon, I suppose, to make sure that nobody gets hurt down at the post office when they carry out their invasion. So, please don't ask me to accept that I'm about to join their ranks. That's impossible. You see, you're either one of them or one of us. And I'm definitely one of us. Besides,

I'm Not Really Retiring

I'm still waiting for . . .

Promotion

Well, I can't just up and go before I finish my career properly. Not the sort of person to do things by halves. Never have been. Okay, I'm not saying it's been an easy job reaching the next rung on the ladder. But if I give up now I'll be throwing forty years of perseverance down the drain. All right, I know it's a long time to go without being recognized but I don't give up that easily. You see, at the top of our building there's a suite of offices that look out over the whole of the city. County, in fact. And the office with the biggest desk, the thickest carpet and most panoramic view belongs to the MD. Always has done. Not the same MD of

Promotion

course. Get a new one every couple of years or so. But the point I'm making is, for any respectable, upwardly mobile guy, that's the natural consequence of his efforts to support the company during the course of his life's work. It's where any self-respecting, conscientious fellow should expect to end up.

I'm Not Really Retiring

And I'm still a floor or two short. Well, four or five actually. So, selecting me for retirement at this crucial developmental stage in my career would be nothing short of commercial suicide. No company in its right mind would entertain the notion. Surely. Strange thing is though, for the past few years the HR

Promotion

department seem to have been guilty of quite monumental errors of judgement when selecting successive MDs. Not my place to comment of course but it has been rather peculiar. You see, they always used to adopt the practice of recruiting MDs of, how can I say?, well, of a certain maturity. People of relatively advancing years with the kind of authority you'd expect. And without exception, older than me. People I could, quite rightly, look up to. But these days age doesn't appear to matter at all. They're quite happy to hand the post to any young upstart. Can you imagine? It's a complete farce. Means I'm

Promotion

totally accountable to some young whippersnapper not long out of high school. Utterly ridiculous. Can't imagine what's in their minds. And as if that's not enough, I'm expected to work my butt off while he's out hobnobbing with important clients on the golf course. Which leads to another reason why I

I'm Not Really Retiring

can't possibly retire . . .

Months and months of the damn stuff. If you could see how much I'm expected to get through you'd realise why the very idea of retirement is out of the question. Totally implausible. The subject just hasn't been thought through properly. Which is absolutely typical of the people running this company at the moment. Soon come to their senses if I were to walk out one afternoon and never come back. Be on the phone pleading with me to return in no time. Thing is, I can remember countless old souls who've retired — hundreds of them over the years — so I know exactly what's involved. Firstly, they've

I'm Not Really Retiring

got to be sufficiently decrepit to render their services of little use to anyone but the local residential care home. Secondly, the rest of the workforce will have grown so intolerant of their very existence that they'll be virtually pushing them out the door. And thirdly, their desk will be devoid of anything remotely more important than memos from the staff welfare department inviting them to attend therapy sessions designed to prepare them and their fellow old codgers for life after work. As if the company gives a damn anyway about what happens to them when they go?

Work

Pleased to see the back of them I should think. Now this isn't helping my workload. Sitting here talking to you all day. Must make some attempt to clear my desk before the boss starts hollering at me. Right, where to begin? Mm, put my packed lunch away first, don't want me sarnies nicked the moment I turn my back. And

I'm Not Really Retiring

what are these things doing here? Stapler, hole punch, pencil sharpener, pocket calculator, empty polystyrene coffee cups. God, what a mess. Shove them all in the drawer. That's better, might stand a chance of seeing what I'm actually supposed to be doing. Now, hold on, let's get rid of these bloody paper clips. Get everywhere. Into the desk tidy I think along with these ball point pens, pencils, Jesus, how many writing implements does a guy need? Take a few of these home — won't be missed by anybody here. Right, that's even better still. Might manage to attend to some of this paperwork at last. Now, what have we got here? Not a lot actually. Must be more up-to-date than I thought. Just three bits of paper. Not bad, eh? People of my calibre must be worth their weight in gold. Can't exactly call three pieces of good old A4 a backlog! Keep the wheels turning. That's what I say. No point in letting it pile up. Sort it out, pass it on and get on with the next task, that's my motto. So, what have we got? Er, next session ten o'clock Wednesday? What's that all about? And what's this? Financial counselling? And this one, I don't believe it, Bus Pass Application Form. This is not funny. Who would have the audacity to leave these on *my* desk? Stay where you are, I'll just go and find out who they're really for. Okay, I'm back. Chucked the things in the bin. Bloody cheek. If I ever find out who . . . no, wait a minute, let me turn the tables on them. I'm jolly well going to attend the next session they have with their . . .

Counsellor

Just for the hell of it. That'll surprise them. Mind you, got to find a way of getting past the doorman. Have to put on a bit of disguise. Make myself look like a real old'n. Should be a laugh if nothing else. Let's see now, need to draw in a few fake lines around the eyes. And add a few more grey hairs, mm, that should do. Oh, and

I'm Not Really Retiring

perhaps adopt a bit of a stoop. Maybe even limp a touch. Got to look convincing. God, poor old souls, look at 'em all. No wonder they're retired — what use would they be to an employer? Thank God I'm not one of them. Right, if you'll just excuse me a minute, I'll perch myself down here, and try to look inconspicuous. Must try to avoid

Counsellor

joining in or they'll twig my more youthful general demeanour. Couldn't possibly come across as a pukka OAP. Well, of all the bloody cheek. It must have been a set up. Somebody taking the pee, no question. There I was minding my own business gate-crashing their silly little therapy session when the snotty-nosed little twit of a counsellor decided to point her sweaty little finger in my direction inviting me, "as an obvious veteran pensioner of some standing", to offer a few words of wisdom to the new recruits. What was she thinking? Put me in a right embarrassing position. Me! The very epitome of eternal

I'm Not Really Retiring

Counsellor

adolescence. Well, maybe that's a bit of an exaggeration but you know what I'm getting at. Don't you? All right, so I overdid the make up. That's my trouble, don't do things by halves. You know as well as I do that had I simply gone in as me I'd have been disqualified from the event. Just wouldn't have looked the part mingling with all those novice wrinklies. Oh well, have to put it down to experience. But at least it gave me an insight into the matter of being an oldie. Could apply to me one day, who knows? And you know the most remarkable thing about the whole bunch of them? Eh? It's their . . .

Clothes

Yeah? You with me? You've seen 'em, haven't you? Nobody else dresses like that. And I've certainly no intention of following suit. Besides, I wouldn't have a clue where to buy those trousers that come half way up your chest. Couldn't be an OAP without at least a couple of pairs of those. May be special government issue I suppose. Definitely haven't seen them in the shops. Probably come with your pension book. Not a bad idea really when you think about it. One of the more positive things to come out of Whitehall I reckon. Mind you, they don't look awfully comfortable, do they? But then there's obviously

I'm Not Really Retiring

Clothes

a need for the postmaster to be able to identify the genuine claimants in the queue each week. After all, anybody could pinch a pension book or two, couldn't they? And if they could just nip round to the high street and kit themselves out with a pair of those high-ribbers the whole system would be wide open to abuse. Good thinking that. Not just pretty faces those politicians. Still, you probably pay through the nose for them what with the amount of pension you actually receive. No such thing as a free lunch (or should that be lunchbox in this case?). Anyway, where was I? Oh yes, clothes. It doesn't stop with government issue trousers.

Clothes

No way. You have to make sure you're not short of Fair Isle tank-tops, carpet slippers (tough enough for regular trips to the local shops), and for more extensive excursions, a sturdy pair of best quality supermarket trainers. None of which you will be likely to find in my wardrobe. Can you imagine? No, no, no; track suits. That's all you'll find there. Well, apart from my work suits of course. High fashion sportswear. Clothes that allow a youngster like me to express his true identity while still remaining at the cutting edge of fashion. All right, I admit I don't do a great deal of running these days. Well,

Clothes

none at all actually. But that's not the point. No, the trendy, sports gear in my wardrobe lets the body move more freely. Keeps it in perfect shape while you're doing no more than strolling down the high street. Keeps you in the right frame of mind. Well, there's nothing wrong with that, is there? You don't have to be an international athlete to wear great gear like that. Of course you don't. And the sports companies recognize that. Look, why would they make the damn things with enough elastic to circumvent my slightly-less-than-trim waistline? Mm, ever thought about that? It's so that all

Clothes

different types of cool dudes like me can demonstrate their obvious agility when it may not be otherwise apparent. Lets everyone know that all of us sporty types belong to the same club whatever our general outward appearance. Another perfect example of why I'm simply not in the running for this retirement nonsense. And there's another thing. If I were to pack up and go home for good how would I get about? You don't think they'd let me take the . . .

I'm Not Really Retiring

Company Car

Do you? Just drive away in a few thousand pounds' worth of their property? Well I certainly don't. An extra portion of chips in the staff canteen is difficult enough to get away with. So how could I deal with not having a car to get around in? If I was ready for retirement I'd have enough dosh in the bank to buy myself a little runabout. You know, nothing too ambitious but big enough and reliable enough to get me and the missus down to the supermarket once a week. But my bank balance wouldn't run to that. Which is further proof that I'm not eligible for this retiring farce. Fact is, I simply haven't had sufficient time to accumulate the

Company Car

readies needed to adapt to a different kind of lifestyle. And my boss knows full well that this is the case. For God's sake it's him who dishes out my salary in the first place. He'd know how impossible it would be for me to fund my own vehicle. They cost a fortune these days. Even modest little OAP-mobiles. Funny thing is though, we've always had a policy here of replacing the fleet cars every two years. Something the firm's accounts insist on for taxable advantages or something like that. Don't ask me, not my subject. But for some strange reason my old jalopy is now edging on towards its third birthday. Poor

Company Car

old thing. No one else in the office seems to have been overlooked. Car park is chock full with nice new shiny motors. Not fair really. Still, I know the real reason. So easy to get things all upside-down, don't you think? Sit there and dwell on things too long and you get them clean out of perspective. Nothing to do with reality at all. We're all guilty of it from time to time aren't we? Human nature. That's all. All think we're being persecuted by someone or other. And more often than not by the boss, yeah? Well, I'm not falling into that trap. Might not be exactly getting on in years but I've enough experience in life

Company Car

to know that things aren't always as they appear. No, it's perfectly obvious to me that I've been singled out as the only employee responsible enough to be trusted to look after the car for more than the regular period. While everybody else is lording it in the golf club bar, I'm taking a far more honourable approach to the whole matter out on the drive with a sponge and a bucket of hot soapy water. Always arrive at the office on Monday morning with the smartest hatchback in the car park. And take it from me, that doesn't go unnoticed. No way. And what's more, it's pretty apparent that the other lot would give their right arms to be as good a driver as me. Honest. They know that and so does the guv'nor. It's nothing to do with age. No, just aptitude. I just happen to be better at it than most people. Probably in my genes. You've heard psychologists speak of motor skills surely? Well that's obviously what I've got. Loads of them. Don't get me wrong, I can't take credit for them myself. Just the lucky recipient of motor genes at birth. And that's exactly where the others miss out. They think they're advantaged by being awarded a bright new status symbol every twenty-four months but I know that my old faithful set of wheels will out

I'm Not Really Retiring

Company Car

last theirs because of the care it is given both on and off the road. Simple. And, of course, my boss knows only too well. Not silly, my boss. Doesn't miss a trick. You know he's even had the foresight to realize that, irrespective of the care and attention it is given, an aging vehicle will still need replacement parts. Only this morning he's sent me an e-mail requesting that I return my set of keys to his office later this morning. He's dead right you know, they're showing positive signs of wear and I could well do with a duplicate set. And people complain about their bosses. I don't know. Here, while we're on the subject, let me tell you

Company Car

about the trouble
he goes to when
it comes to the
matter of . . .

Holidays

Not the mean old so-'n'-so you'd expect him to be. Quite the reverse. Well, at least he has been recently. The department has always operated the same way with senior members of staff automatically taking precedence over intermediate and junior levels. Experience and loyalty come first. No argument. Plain

Holidays

and simple hierarchical logic. Common sense if you like. If you've been here a couple of months and you've booked your hols at an inconvenient time then tough luck. You go to the back of the queue, like it or not. And even if you think you're in the privileged position of having totted up more than a few years of service, it's bad news if you can't fit in with your superiors. I can remember one chap some years ago, God, it must have been three or four decades ago, anyway no sooner had he taken up his post than he announced his intention to swan off to some exotic location during the self same weeks that the guv'nor had arranged his

Holidays

annual vacation. No chance. Trouble was his better half had no alternative either and ended up storming into the office to give the boss what for. Quite a dish if my memory serves me correctly and made one hell of a scene as you can imagine. But no good came of it. Well not for the young upstart anyway. In fact it didn't stop there for the poor little sod. The boss took one look at the advancing brunette, picked up the phone and delivered some cock and bull story to his better half and duly escorted the young lady to the predestined location for the duration of the prescribed two weeks. If that didn't teach our new recruit a lesson nothing

Holidays

would. However, I digress. The point is, this year, for some reason or other, Mr. B came over all compliant when the subject of holidays was mentioned and with a great, big smile on his face, suggested that I could choose whatever weeks I wished. And if they weren't enough, I was to be allowed to repeat the exercise as many times as I saw fit. Can you believe that? Is that a reasonable man or is that a reasonable man? I was naturally dumbstruck. Taken completely off my guard and, although my memory of the event remains something of a blur, I do believe I, quite embarrassingly, curtsied on my way out of his room. All right, I

Holidays

wasn't thinking clearly and made a right ass of myself but he deserved whatever means I chose or unwittingly elected to employ as an expression of my gratitude. Won't be long now actually. Can't wait. And it even looks as though I'll have a brand new set of keys to ensure the car won't break down before we arrive at our destination. Yippee, yippee! Life's not so bad when you come to think of it, is it? Thank God I'm not up for this retirement rubbish. Can't imagine anything more demoralizing than actually seeing your name printed on the front of a . . .

I'm Not Really Retiring

Pension Book

Heads and ovens time I would think. Well, only metaphorically, of course. Wouldn't want to unnecessarily depress any poor old soul who might actually be approaching retirement. But I mean, there you are, working away happily, doing your bit for the nation's GDP, enjoying a sense of purpose each time you put in another day's graft then, right out of the blue: ZONK, off you go — carriage clock and all. Your gait shortens, your back hunches and your head examines the cracks in the paving stones all the way home. The missus can't get a word out of you all evening and you down the entire contents of the malted bevy you brought back

I'm Not Really Retiring

from last year's holiday in the highlands. Then, as if the next morning's hangover isn't enough to contend with, that infernal little postie fellow trots merrily up the front garden path for the sole purpose of rubbing neat sodium chloride into your gaping flesh by popping twelve months' worth of miserable little vouchers through the letterbox. The little sod. And it's no good him protesting that he's only doing his job because he's an integral cog in the whole bloody wheel that euphemistically describes itself as the welfare system. Welfare my foot. It's no more than a conspiracy to control the old buggers and stop them enjoying themselves. I'm not fooled that easily. Though, of course, not actually being directly affected, I can't help feeling a certain sympathy with them. After all, sometime in the future it could be me. You never know. Sounds a bit far-fetched, I'll grant you, but even *I* will reach retirement age one day. And when that day

I'm Not Really Retiring

arrives I'd like to think somebody would do the same for me. Even if each week's tear-out slip will only get me through two, or three, days before I'll have to start dipping into the savings to put some food on the table. Anyway, enough of this musing — I'm beginning to get depressed myself. Anyone would think that *I'm* about to retire. Anyway, it seems like I've been sitting here for hours deliberating over the poor old souls' misfortunes while I'm supposed to be working. So, if you'll excuse me, I must get on with something more productive. Don't want to be kicked out before I reach the dreaded day. But thanks for listening. I really

I'm Not Really Retiring

do appreciate it. Honest. But . . . hold on a sec . . . hey, what's going on here? Sorry but . . . what on earth do they think they're doing? You're not going to believe this but what would appear to be the sum total of the company's workforce have just walked into my office dressed in party hats. And half of them are carrying trays with glasses and bottles of bubbly on them. I've never seen anything like it in my life. Well, not in *my* office I haven't. They've all gone stark raving mental. The lot of them. You'll have to excuse me, I must go and find out what is going on here.

Other Not Really Titles . . .

I'M NOT REALLY PREGNANT
Don't even go there. If I was ready to be pregnant I'd be a mum kind of person. And I'm not. I'm much too young for anything like that. Besides, I've been taking precautions. And so has my partner. I think. So it would be a physical impossibility. And, what's more, I don't eat funny food or have a mum and dad who look anything like grandparents. No, preggers is definitely for other people.

Other Not Really Titles . . .

I'M NOT REALLY MOVING HOUSE
Just because there's a 'For Sale' board outside my house it doesn't mean that someone is going to want to buy it. I don't get fooled that easily. It's actually a free advertisement for a local estate agent who's too busy selling everybody else's houses to bother himself about mine. It'll probably still be there in five years' time. No, I can't possibly be moving house, that only happens to other people.

Other Not Really Titles . . .

I'M NOT REALLY GETTING MARRIED
Married? What am I thinking? Of course I'm not getting married. I'm a single girl, after all. Always have been. Married people are nothing like me. They're more serious than me. Want to dedicate their lives to washing and ironing. And doing all sorts of boring housework. And having babies for God's sake. I must sort this awful mess out – I can't possibly be getting married – marriage is for other people.

Other Not Really Titles . . .

Other Not Really Titles . . .

Forthcoming Titles . . .